LIVING OUT OF THE OVERFLOW

SERVING OUT OF YOUR INTIMACY WITH GOD

WORKBOOK

Dr. Richard Blackaby

with John Watkins

Blackaby Ministries International

Jonesboro, Georgia

LIVING OUT OF THE OVERFLOW: SERVING OUT OF YOUR INTIMACY WITH GOD
WORKBOOK
PUBLISHED BY BLACKABY MINISTRIES INTERNATIONAL
P.O. Box 1035
Jonesboro, GA 30237
www.blackaby.org

ISBN 978-1-7320939-2-8

Publisher's Cataloging-in-Publication data

Names: Blackaby, Richard, 1961-, author. | Watkins, John, author.
Title: Living out of the overflow : serving out of your intimacy with God Workbook/ Dr. Richard Blackaby with John Watkins
Description: No bibliographical references | Jonesboro, GA: Blackaby Ministries International, 2019.
Identifiers: ISBN 9978-1-7320939-2-8 | LCCN 2018913590
Subjects: LCSH Christian life. | Spiritual life--Christianity. | God (Christianity)--Knowableness. | BISAC RELIGION / Christian Life / General
Classification: LCC BV4501.3 .B534 2019 | DDC 248.4--dc23

Printed in the United States of America
2019 — 1st ed

Contents

INTRODUCTION

Several years ago, I was invited to speak to a group of church leaders. I searched Scripture for passages that would encourage those faithful people who had suffered much as they served the Lord. God led me to examine three chapters from the Bible that describe the lives of Elijah and Moses. I unpacked those chapters verse by verse, and the result was astounding. The audience was transfixed. People cried. Many attendees told me the two saints' stories greatly encouraged them. I have since traveled around the world sharing these truths, and the result is always the same.

Over time, many people have asked me to provide a study guide to accompany the *Living out of the Overflow* book so groups of people can study the material together. This workbook is the answer to that request.

Here are some guidelines that will help you maximize the benefits of this study. First, this workbook is not a substitute for the book *Living Out of the Overflow*. Both the book and the workbook are necessary.

Second, the workbook is most effective when completed in a small group setting. Scripture says, "Then those who feared the Lord spoke to one another, and the Lord listened and heard them. So a book of remembrance was written before Him for those who fear the Lord and who meditate on His name" (Mal. 3:16). Something powerful happens when people study God's Word together.

Third, do not skip the assignments. Prior to meeting with your group, complete the assigned reading from *Living out of the Overflow*, answer the questions at the end of each chapter and in the workbook under the "Connect" and "Overflow" headings, and do the exercises listed in the "Accountability" section. Do not rush your responses or neglect the exercises. If you do, you will miss some of the richest aspects of this study.

Fourth, attend and participate in your small group sessions. Assume that God put your group together and that each member plays a vital role. Pray before each session. Prepare your heart so you are ready to give and to receive. Each time you uncover an insight about what God intends for His people, stop and ask yourself, "Does my life reflect this biblical truth?" Don't be satisfied until it does.

Welcome to the *Living Out of the Overflow* workbook. I pray it encourages you, deepens your walk with Christ, and makes you a more effective, joyful servant of God.

A NOTE ON THE VARIOUS SECTIONS OF THIS WORKBOOK

The **Accountability** sections are to be completed in advance and ready to share at the next group meeting. The **Connect** sections are intended to help reveal where you are on your journey with Christ. Finally, the **Overflow** sections are there to help you take the next step based on what God reveals to you during this study.

A NOTE ON VIDEOS

In addition to this workbook, this study also has optional videos/DVDs that provide teachings by Richard Blackaby for each group session. The videos can be found in the BMI Resource store (www.blackabystore.org) or you can contact BMI for more information (resources@blackaby.org).

LIVING OUT OF THE OVERFLOW

SERVING OUT OF YOUR INTIMACY WITH GOD

INTRODUCTORY SESSION

INTRODUCTORY SESSION

The enormous challenges believers face today can leave them feeling spiritually desolate and thirsty. Christ's followers function in a society that is increasingly secular, scoffs at God's Word, and adamantly rejects His standards. People are enamored with worldly pleasures, permeated by self-centered ideology, and in bondage to sin. The percentage of people who hold a biblical worldview continues to dwindle. The media celebrates sins society once considered scandalous. If believers allow their faith to become parched, they will be in constant danger of stumbling and falling.

In eras that have experienced increased public immorality, violence, crime, and broken homes, the Church has generally heralded God's message of hope. Today, however, the Church is in critical condition itself. Roughly 70 percent of churches in America are plateaued or in decline. Thousands of churches are disbanding each year. Simply trying harder will not suffice. The Church should not continue using the same ineffective methods. It needs people who are willing to surrender themselves wholly to God's power and might so they are prepared to strike a mighty blow for His kingdom.

The encouraging reality for today's spiritual leaders is that God has a solution for every problem. No matter how ferocious the enemy, God's power is greater. Regardless of the evil machinations of the powers of darkness, God's wisdom is superior. The question is whether Christians are willing to remain obedient as He fashions them into effective instruments for His good. God is the master of taking people from where they are to where He wants them to be. He delights in using ordinary people to accomplish extraordinary tasks. Believers must decide if they intend to continue ministering ineffectively in their own strength and wisdom or if they are prepared to become a powerful tool in God's hand.

CONNECT

Ask someone to read Ephesians 3:20.

As a group, spend time discussing each person's answers to the following questions:

➤ What worldly traps have you fallen into or are you currently striving to avoid?

➤ What does this verse say about God's power in today's secular society?

➤ How is God currently doing "exceedingly abundantly" in your life?

CHALLENGE

God gave His Son the most difficult assignment in human history. To prepare Jesus for the cross, the Father took Him to a mountaintop. Jesus brought His three closest companions with Him to that sacred mount. The Father also summoned two saints from history—Moses and Elijah. He could have retrieved anyone from any age to encourage His Son, so His choice is noteworthy.

Moses represented the law; Elijah represented the prophets. Yet the Father's choice held even greater significance. Moses and Elijah had much in common with Jesus. Their lives were punctuated by mountaintop experiences. Fierce enemies opposed them. They spent time in the wilderness. God accomplished miracles through them. They worked with people who wavered in faith and resisted God's commands. In the Father's infinite wisdom, He knew these men could encourage His Son as He prepared for His greatest challenge.

CONNECT

➤ Read 1 Kings 18 as a group.

➤ In 1 Kings 18:37-38, Elijah knew he was a dead man if God did not act. Have you ever been in a situation so dire that life's problems would have consumed you if God had not intervened? If so, share your experience with the group and explain how God's power brought you through it.

INVITATION

Join us on our own mountaintop. Allow Moses and Elijah to undergird you in the same way they encouraged Jesus. Proverbs 13:20 promises that if we walk with wise people, we will become wise. In this study, we will draw near to two inspirational biblical leaders.

This workbook is supplemental to the book *Living Out of The Overflow: Serving Out of Your Intimacy with God,* and it is most effective when completed in a small group setting. Group members should prepare for each session, keep conversations confidential, and, most importantly, allow the Holy Spirit to speak into their life. Meeting on a consistent basis is important so group members can encourage each other, keep each other accountable, and discuss what God is teaching them. Groups can meet weekly, monthly, or for a weekend retreat.

Before each meeting, read specific pages in *Living Out of The Overflow: Serving Out of Your Intimacy with God*, prayerfully work through the **overflow application questions** from the previous session, and spend time each day in God's Word.

OVERFLOW

Answer the following questions before your next session:

➤ What is holding me back from becoming a more effective servant of God?

➤ What is God currently trying to teach me about Himself, myself, and those I serve?

➤ Have I spent too much time focusing on my problems and too little time deepening my relationship with God? What adjustments should I make so I can spend more time with God?

Your effectiveness as a spiritual leader is directly correlated to the vibrancy of your walk with God. We pray that as you deepen your relationship with Him, you will develop an insatiable hunger to become the leader God designed you to be. Furthermore, we pray that spending time with Moses and Elijah will make you long for God to use you as mightily as He used them.

ACCOUNTABILITY

Complete before your next small group session:

➤ Spend time prayerfully reviewing and answering the questions from this session.

➤ Read Section 1, Chapters 1 and 2 in *Living Out of The Overflow: Serving Out of Your Intimacy with God.*

LIVING OUT OF THE OVERFLOW

SERVING OUT OF YOUR INTIMACY WITH GOD

GROUP SESSION 1: FAITHFUL LIVING

GROUP SESSION 1: FAITHFUL LIVING

ACCOUNTABILITY

Discuss your answers from the *OVERFLOW* section in the **Introductory Session:**

➤ What is holding me back from becoming a more effective servant of God?

➤ What is God currently teaching me about His character, myself, and those I lead?

➤ Have I spent too much time focusing on my problems and too little time deepening my relationship with God? What adjustments should I make so I can spend more time with God?

Deepening your relationship with God is essential to living out of the overflow. God has provided everything you need to be filled with His living water

(John 4:14). He desires for you to abide in Him each day so you are prepared for your next assignment.

"When God intends to accomplish a great work through His servants, He always prepares them. Not everyone is willing to remain in God's school of faith and prayer until God's work is complete" (*Overflow*, 4). God delights in using ordinary people to accomplish His perfect plan. God used the prophet Elijah, a regular person, in extraordinary ways.

AN ORDINARY PERSON

Now Elijah the Tishbite, from the Gilead settlers, said to Ahab, "As the Lord God of Israel lives, I stand before Him, and there will be no dew or rain during these years except by my command!" (1 Kings 17:1)

Elijah may be the greatest prophet of the Old Testament, yet he appears suddenly with no fanfare. He is from Tishbe, a village so insignificant archaeologists are uncertain of its location. No village of Tishbe has been found in Gilead, although there is one farther north in Naphtali. Clearly, people's hometown, alma mater, or socio-economic status plays no determining factor in how mightily God can use them. With God, where you are going matters far more than where you started.

Elijah's statement in verse one serves as his only qualification: "As the Lord God of Israel lives, I stand before Him." Elijah's influence stemmed not from his credentials or experience but from his time in God's presence. Elijah knew what was on God's heart and mind. Never underestimate the power of knowing God's will.

CONNECT

➤ What insecurities might hinder you from serving the Lord?

➤ Does your past or level of education or inexperience ever cause you to lower your expectations for what God can accomplish through you? If so, explain these feelings to the group.

A DIFFICULT ASSIGNMENT

God gave Elijah the exceedingly difficult assignment of preaching an unwelcome message to a hostile congregation. Ahab was the most wicked king ever to rule the nation (1 Kings 16:33). Encouraged by his evil wife, Jezebel, Ahab exterminated God's prophets and promoted Baal worship throughout the nation.

God sent Elijah to warn Ahab that there would be a drought. Why a drought? Because Baal was the god of the storm. He promised to give farmers rain if they pledged their loyalty to him. God declared war on His people's idol. The news would devastate the evil king whose prosperity depended on his nation's farmers having good crops. Elijah must have wondered if he would leave the royal court alive. Nevertheless, he faithfully delivered God's warning.

God's servants do not have the luxury of choosing their message. They must not tone it down or make it more palatable. While God's messengers should strive to be gracious, the primary measure of their success is how accurately they deliver their divine decree.

CONNECT

> ➤ As you sought God's will, what message or assignment did He give you to deliver or accomplish?

> ➤ How has fear of a difficult reception kept you from being obedient to your divine assignment?

> ➤ Is there any area where you have not been obedient to God's direction in your life? If so, explain.

Then a revelation from the Lord came to him; "Leave here, turn eastward, and hide yourself at the Wadi Cherith where it enters the Jordan. You are to drink from the wadi. I have commanded the ravens to provide for you there." So he did what the Lord commanded. Elijah left and lived by the Wadi Cherith where it enters the Jordan. The ravens kept bringing him bread and meat in the morning and in the evening, and he drank from the wadi. (1 Kings 17:2-6)

CONSIGNED TO A WILDERNESS

Sometimes God orders His servants to charge into battle. At other times, He commands them to withdraw from the fray. Elijah obeyed God's instructions to the letter. His reward? The wilderness.

Most people view the wilderness as a place of punishment. God consigned the unbelieving Israelites to a wilderness for 40 years because of their lack of faith. By sending Elijah into hiding, God appeared to be punishing His faithful servant. But God views the wilderness differently than people do. He was still speaking into Elijah's life (1 King 17:2). The prophet's obedience to flee into the wilderness, as unfair and undeserved as the command might have seemed, was evidence of Elijah's great faith. After Jesus' baptism, His Father consigned Him to a wilderness for 40 days (Matthew 3:15-4:2). Elijah's story provides another example of how God can use the wilderness to prepare His servants for their next assignment. Many everyday distractions and competing voices are absent in the wilderness. In the wilderness, God has people's full attention.

CONNECT

➤   Describe a time when you obeyed God and your life became more difficult as a result.

➤ Describe a time when you thought God was handling your life unfairly. How did the experience affect you? If you're married, how did it affect your spouse?

➤ Describe a time when you fought after God told you to withdraw. Describe a time when you withdrew when God commanded you to fight. What prompted you to disobey God's instructions?

We should not assume every difficult circumstance we experience is a punishment. Though challenges might indicate we have sinned, they could also be part of God's assignment. Our expectations lead to disappointment when we view situations from our perspective rather than God's. We should not do God's work our way and expect supernatural results. If we are faithfully walking with God, we can be assured that He always has a plan for our future.

OVERFLOW

➤ When have you found yourself in a spiritual wilderness? How did you handle it?

➤ What have you learned in the wilderness?

➤ Do you regularly find a quiet place to listen to God? Describe what makes that place special.

GOD'S PROVISION

During Elijah's stint in the wilderness, he interacted solely with ravens and God. Birds delivered the prophet's meals each morning and evening. Why did God send provisions twice per day? After all, God sent manna to the Israelites in the wilderness only once daily. The reason may be that God was merely sustaining the Israelites, but He was preparing Elijah. Twice per day, Elijah experienced God's clockwork provision. His life depended on it.

God's ways are not our ways. If we were God, we would not consign our best preacher to a wilderness where no sermons were required. Doing so seems like a waste of a good prophet. But God always prepares His servants before using them mightily.

ACCOUNTABILITY

Complete before your next small group session:

➤ Find a quiet place to meet with God. Be prepared to tell your group about your experience in that place at the next meeting.

➤ Spend time prayerfully reviewing and answering the questions from this session.

➤ Read Section 1, Chapters 3-4 in *Living Out of The Overflow: Serving Out of Your Intimacy with God.*

LIVING OUT OF THE OVERFLOW

SERVING OUT OF YOUR INTIMACY WITH GOD

GROUP SESSION 2: LIVING DESPERATELY

GROUP SESSION 2: LIVING DESPERATELY

ACCOUNTABILITY

Discuss your answers from the *OVERFLOW* section in **Group Session 1:**

➤ When have you found yourself in a spiritual wilderness? How did you handle it?

➤ What have you learned in the wilderness?

➤ Describe a time you spent in a place of quiet and solitude since your last group session.

The wilderness has negative connotations. God sentenced the Israelites to the wilderness because of their disobedience and lack of faith. We might assume nothing good could happen in such a place. But the wilderness provides peace and quiet. It is free from distractions. Our time in the wilderness can help us determine our priorities. It can stimulate healing and renew our strength before God grants us a new assignment.

When we are in a wilderness, we typically have more time than when we are busily engaged in our work. During our normal routines, we often fail to spend adequate time with God. We may think devoting a few moments each morning to reading Scripture and asking God to bless our day is sufficient. But how much time should we spend in quiet and solitude? Someone once asked Dr. Henry Blackaby how long he spent with his Lord each morning. Blackaby's answer was simple but profound: "Until God is finished."

We might feel tempted to tell God when we have completed our wilderness experience. But as willing servants, we must trust that we are in the place where God wants us. At the right time, He will lead us to take our next step. We should emulate Elijah. He persevered in a tough assignment until God gave him new instructions.

➤ Why might your circumstances seem to get worse while you wait for God's direction? Would you still trust Him?

THINGS GETTING WORSE

After a while, the wadi dried up because there had been no rain in the land. (1 Kings 17:7)

God gave Elijah an extremely difficult assignment, and he obeyed it to the letter. As a result, he was forced to retreat into a wilderness. He trusted God fully in the wilderness, and his water ran dry. Each time Elijah obeyed God, his life became more difficult!

CONNECT

➤ Are you currently waiting for a word from the Lord? If so, what were the last instructions He gave you? Are you being obedient?

➤ Is the water in your wadi drying up? How are you handling the wait?

➤ Why do you think God is asking you to wait?

Notice what God said to Elijah: *"Then the word of the Lord came to Elijah"* (1 Kings 17:8). God didn't give Elijah instructions until he needed them! Could God have alerted Elijah weeks earlier that the wadi would eventually dry up and he would have to relocate? Yes, but God chose to wait until the last possible moment to inform His premier prophet of his next move.

Then the word of the Lord came to him: "Get up, go to Zarephath that belongs to Sidon, and stay there. Look, I have commanded a woman who is a widow to provide for you there." So Elijah got up and went to Zarephath. (1 Kings 17:8-9)

We would think that following God out of a difficult situation would lead to a season of victory. But Elijah followed God's instructions out of the wilderness and into circumstances that proved to be quite humbling.

When he arrived at the city gate, there was a widow woman gathering wood. Elijah called to her and said, "Please bring me a little water in a cup and let me drink." As she went to get it, he called to her and said, "Please bring me a piece of bread in your hand."

But she said, "As the Lord your God lives, I don't have anything baked—only a handful of flour in the jar and a bit of oil in the jug. Just now, I am gathering a couple of sticks in order to go prepare it for myself and my son so we can eat it and die."

Then Elijah said to her, "Don't be afraid; go and do as you have said. But first make me a small loaf from it and bring it out to me. Afterward, you may make some for yourself and your son, for this is what the LORD GOD OF ISRAEL SAYS, 'The flour jar will not become empty and the oil jug will not run dry until the day the Lord sends rain on the surface of the land.'"

So she proceeded to do according to the word of Elijah. Then the woman, Elijah, and her household ate for many days. The flour jar did not become empty, and the oil jug did not run dry, according to the word of the Lord He had spoken through Elijah. (1 Kings 17:10-16)

ASSIGNED TO HUMBLE CIRCUMSTANCES

God commanded Elijah to go to Zarapeth, a Gentile city near Sidon that was the epicenter of Baal worship. A widow would care for him there. These instructions were unimaginably humiliating for a righteous Jewish man. He would have to ask for charity from an impoverished, starving Gentile widow who worshipped Baal. Elijah's circumstances could seemingly not sink any lower. Surely God could have provided for His most effective servant in a more dignified manner. But He did not. "God's primary concern for His servants is never what they are doing but who they are becoming" (*Overflow*, 38). God continued to mold and shape Elijah. The size of the assignment was not as important to God as the state of His servant's heart.

CONNECT

➤ How do you respond when God places you in a position where you must rely on other people's generosity?

➤ Recall a time when God provided for you in an unusual manner. How well did you receive that provision?

➤ Elijah was the greatest preacher of his day, and he was assigned to a congregation of two. If you serve in a leadership role in a small setting, how faithfully are you carrying out your assignment?

NEEDING A MIRACLE

Assuming your situation cannot get worse is foolish. After the prophet lived in the widow's home for a while, the widow's son died. The experience must have been devastating. Surely Elijah had urged the woman to trust in the God of Israel. He must have assured her that God loved her and had a wonderful plan for her life. But God allowed her only child to die.

After this, the son of the woman who owned the house became ill. His illness became very severe until no breath remained in him. She said to Elijah, "Man of God, what do we have in common? Have you come to remind me of my guilt and to kill my son?" (1 Kings 17:17-18)

When will this end? Why is life so difficult? These questions are natural responses to challenging life circumstances. But Elijah's reaction stemmed from his intimate walk with God and his deep understanding and trust in God's character.

"For God understands each person's limit. He made us. He knows our capacity for both suffering and faith. He does not intend to crush or demoralize us. Yet He also recognizes that unless He takes us to the end of ourselves, we will never experience the full measure of His grace and power" (*Overflow*, 46).

God placed Elijah in a situation where he could do nothing on his own. He could find his answer only in God's power and presence.

CONNECT

➤ Do you currently need a miracle? How are you handling your situation?

In her grief, the widow pointed an accusing finger at Elijah and bitterly assailed him. Elijah returned to his room with the boy and cried out to the Lord. The difference between saying a prayer and crying out to the Lord is profound! Elijah prayed over the boy three times. Why three? Because that is how many times it took for the boy's life to return. Only then did the widow trust in Elijah's God.

But Elijah said to her, "Give me your son." So he took him from her arms, brought him up to the upper room where he was staying, and laid him on his own bed. Then he cried out to the Lord and said, "My Lord God, have You also brought tragedy on the widow I am staying with by killing her son?" Then he stretched himself out over the boy three times. He cried out to the Lord and said, "My Lord God, please let this boy's life return to him!"

So the Lord listened to Elijah's voice, and the boy's life returned to him, and he lived. Then Elijah took the boy, brought him down from the upper room into the house, and gave him to his mother. Elijah said, "Look, your son is alive." Then the woman said to Elijah, "Now I know you are a man of God and the Lord's word in your mouth is the truth." (1 Kings 17:19-24)

DON'T GIVE UP

In the next chapter, Elijah will stand atop Mount Carmel and boldly challenge 850 prophets of Baal and Asherah to a showdown of strength. How did Elijah know fire would fall from heaven when he prayed? Because he had just spent three-and-a-half years in God's school of faith and prayer.

OVERFLOW

➤ Are you currently crying out to the Lord? How urgent are your prayers?

➤ List some of your current prayer requests. With what intensity are you praying for these needs?

Many believers desire to have a ministry as powerful as Elijah's. But how many people are willing to let God prepare them in His school of faith? "Only heaven knows how many great men and women of God the Church has lost because they could not endure the refining fires God passed them through" (*Overflow*, 49).

ACCOUNTABILITY

Complete before your next small group session:

➤ Find a place of quiet and solitude and ask God to show you if there is anything in your heart and life that is hindering your prayers (Refer to *Overflow*, 53).

➤ Spend time prayerfully reviewing and answering the questions from this session.

➤ Read Section 2, Chapters 5 and 6 in *Living Out of The Overflow: Serving Out of Your Intimacy with God*.

LIVING OUT OF THE OVERFLOW

SERVING OUT OF YOUR INTIMACY WITH GOD

GROUP SESSION 3: OUR ACHILLES' HEEL

GROUP SESSION 3: OUR ACHILLES' HEEL

ACCOUNTABILITY

Discuss your answers from the *OVERFLOW* section in **Group Session 2**:

➤ List some specific prayer requests. With what intensity are you praying for these needs?

➤ Describe a time you spent in a place of quiet and solitude since the last group session.

Victories, mountaintop experiences, and significant accomplishments can provide satisfaction and a sense of purpose. But what happens during the time between monumental achievements? Should we dwell on these experiences from our past for years to come? People often fixate on the glory days and assume nothing in the future could compare. "Preparing for a great undertaking is one thing. Continuing to find meaning in life after a significant accomplishment is another" (*Overflow*, 61).

God will always provide new opportunities to trust Him. Normal day-to-day challenges can strengthen our walk with God and enable us to live out of the overflow of our relationship with Him.

UNHINGED

Ahab told Jezebel everything that Elijah had done and how he had killed all the prophets with the sword. So Jezebel sent a messenger to Elijah, saying, "May the gods punish me and do so severely if I don't make your life like the life of one of them by this time tomorrow!" (1 Kings 19:1-2)

Our fears change over time. We might feel invincible one moment and consumed with worry the next. Elijah fearlessly served his Lord for more than three years. He witnessed amazing miracles and experienced years of God's faithful provision. But after two of his most spectacular successes, he suddenly succumbed to fear. He fled 112 miles from Jezreel to Beersheba. Then he dismissed his servant and retreated into the desert. He sought to withdraw so far from ministry that his enemies could not find him and God would no longer call on him.

"When Elijah based his life on God's word, there was a serenity and peace about his life, even when he faced difficult circumstances. But now his actions are being driven by the voices of people. And not just any people but his worst enemy" (*Overflow*, 74).

CONNECT

➤ List the types of people and situations that most irritate or discourage you.

➤ How has fear driven your daily life and ministry in the past or present?

➤ Have you ever withdrawn from service without God's permission? Why? What were the consequences?

QUITTING

Then Elijah became afraid and immediately ran for his life. When he came to Beer-sheba that belonged to Judah, he left his servant there, but he went on a day's journey into the wilderness. He sat down under a broom tree and prayed that he might die. He said, "I have had enough! Lord, take my life, for I'm no better than my fathers." Then he lay down and slept under the broom tree. (1 Kings 19:3-5a)

Elijah was determined to quit his prophetic ministry and perhaps his life. He declared that God was all-powerful, but his quitting made a more profound theological statement than his creed did. By deserting, he proclaimed that even God could not give him victory. He turned his gaze from God to his enemies and found himself in a vulnerable position.

Unsurprisingly, Elijah dismissed his servant. When we are wallowing in self-pity, we typically don't want anyone else around who might challenge our self-centered, defeatist point of view. Elijah was so weary and discouraged he said he wanted to die. Of course, he did not really want to die. If he had, he would not have run so fervently for his life. But he wanted his life to change. He was clearly tired of constantly dealing with enemies.

"At times, God changes our circumstances to enable us to better manage our load. On other occasions, rather than change our situation, God changes us. Though our life remains difficult, God grants us the grace and strength to endure it" (*Overflow*, 86).

CONNECT

➤ Describe a time when you considered quitting. Why did you want to quit instead of working toward a solution?

➤ Are you spending more time focusing on problems or on your Lord?

➤ Describe a time when you isolated yourself from friends or fellow believers. Why did you pull away? What were the consequences?

➤ How much time do you currently spend with people who speak truth into your life?

RESTORATION

Suddenly, an angel touched him. The angel told him, "Get up and eat." Then he looked, and there at his head was a loaf of bread baked over hot stones and a jug of water. So he ate and drank and lay down again. Then the angel of the Lord returned a second time and touched him. He said, "Get up and eat, or the journey will be too much for you." So he got up, ate, and drank. Then on the strength from that food, he walked 40 days and 40 nights to Horeb, the mountain of God. (1 Kings 19:5b-8)

God restores discouraged servants. Elijah awoke to the smell of bread baking. An angel touched him, fed him, and encouraged him to rest. The angel did not discuss Elijah's future. For that, he would have to speak directly with God. Then Elijah commenced a 40-day, 200-mile trek to Mt. Sinai, the awesome mount that had terrified the Israelites generations before. Elijah had become so discouraged he needed a life-changing experience with God. Mt. Sinai was the ideal place for such a meeting. Elijah fasted for the next 40 days in solitude as he prepared to encounter his God. His future hinged on that meeting. As we have seen, Elijah spent the better part of his ministry preparing for his next divine encounter.

OVERFLOW

> ➤ What strikes you about how the angel ministered to Elijah? Which are you currently lacking: nourishing food, rest, personal encouragement, or a word from God?

> ➤ What needs to change in your life to fill this need?

"As we read this account, we know in our hearts that God will do everything necessary to reclaim His discouraged servant. The question is not whether God can redeem a difficult situation but whether God's servant will trust in God's provision" (*Overflow*, 94). Has your heart been deceived into thinking God cannot use you because you have run from Him? Have you allowed fear to overwhelm your thoughts and prevent you from obeying God's instructions? In order to live out of the overflow, we must plug holes of fear, deception, and lack of trust and allow God to fill us with rest, truth, and power.

ACCOUNTABILITY

Complete before your next small group session:

> ➤ Where do you go when you need a fresh encounter with God? Go to that place and take time to commune with Him.

➤   What distractions do you need to put aside until God gives you a fresh vision for your life and ministry?

➤   Spend time prayerfully reviewing and answering the questions from this session.

➤   Read Section 2, Chapters 7 – 9 in *Living Out of The Overflow: Serving Out of Your Intimacy with God.*

LIVING OUT OF THE OVERFLOW

SERVING OUT OF YOUR INTIMACY WITH GOD

GROUP SESSION 4: RESTORED

GROUP SESSION 4: RESTORED

ACCOUNTABILITY

Discuss your answers from the *OVERFLOW* section in **Group Session 3**:

➤ What life changes have you made to meet your need for healthy food, rest, and personal encouragement?

➤ What distractions did you put aside in order to hear God clearly?

➤ Describe a time you spent in a place of quiet and solitude since the last group session.

WHAT ARE YOU DOING HERE?

What am I doing here? How did I get here? Have you ever asked yourself those questions? If we are discouraged or fearful, we have clearly shifted our focus from our Lord to something or someone else. As we saw in Elijah's story, even God's premier servants can end up far from where God wants them to be.

Elijah demonstrated how quickly someone can fall from the height of success into a pit of despair.

He entered a cave there and spent the night. Then the word of the Lord came to him, and He said to him, "What are you doing here, Elijah?" He replied, "I have been very zealous for the Lord God of Hosts, but the Israelites have abandoned Your covenant, torn down Your altars, and killed Your prophets with the sword. I alone am left, and they are looking for me to take my life." (1 Kings 19:9-10)

Elijah fled to a cave on Mount Sinai. We can only wonder if he chose the same cleft in the rock where Moses encountered God's glory centuries earlier (Exodus 33:22). Moses was weary from ministering to stiff-necked people, and he longed for a fresh encounter with God. Many years later, Elijah found a cave and waited. He had tried to remedy the situation on his own. Instead of remaining in the place where God placed him, he ran. Elijah had seemed invincible on Mount Carmel. But huddled in a cave on Mount Sinai, Elijah demonstrated that he, too, was vulnerable to fear and failure when he became disoriented to his Lord.

When God came to Elijah in the cave, He asked a simple question: "What are you doing here, Elijah?" God's questions have a way of laying us bare. We may have all manner of justifications for our actions and attitudes, but one question from God can send our defenses tumbling down. When we discover the answer to God's question, we find the answer to ours as well. God might ask the same of you. Are you currently in the place where God intends for you to be?

CONNECT

➤ Have you ever been in a dark, gloomy place? How did you get there? How did God minister to you there?

➤ Have you sensed God asking you, "What are you doing here?" What is your response?

Elijah blamed his situation on his circumstances rather than taking responsibility for his actions. He told God, "Your altars . . . Your prophets." Then he attempted to earn sympathy by lamenting, "I alone am left." Elijah lost focus, and he was trying to find relief. "Our obedience to God's will has nothing to do with other people" (*Overflow*, 103). We should not act based on what we see but based on what God says. We can vent all day long, but nothing will change until we hear from God.

➤ Are you blaming someone else or your circumstances for your disobedience?

"Elijah had lost his spiritual focus. As long as he kept his eyes on his Lord, Elijah saw his circumstances clearly. But the moment he shifted his attention to his problems, he became disoriented to the truth" (*Overflow*, 104).

➤ What steps do you need to take to refocus your heart and mind on the truth?

A STILL, SMALL VOICE

Then He said, "Go out and stand on the mountain in the Lord's presence." At that moment, the Lord passed by. A great and mighty wind was tearing at the mountains and was shattering cliffs before the Lord, but the Lord was not in the wind. After the wind there was an earthquake, but the Lord was not in the earthquake. After the earthquake there was a fire, but the Lord was not in the fire. And after the fire there was a voice, a soft whisper. When Elijah heard it, he wrapped his face in his mantle and went out and stood at the entrance of the cave.

Suddenly, a voice came to him and said, "What are you doing here, Elijah?"

"I have been very zealous for the Lord God of Hosts," he replied, "but the Israelites have abandoned Your covenant, torn down Your altars, and killed Your prophets with the sword. I alone am left, and they're looking for me to take my life." (1 Kings 19:11-14)

What God does is important. How He does something is equally as crucial. A great and mighty wind passed, but God was not in the wind. Then a mighty earthquake, but God was not in it. Then fire, but still God did not speak. Finally, God communicated in a whisper. He told Elijah to leave the cave (1

Kings 19:11). Why didn't God deal with Elijah where He found him? Because all Elijah could see in the cave was darkness and shadows. He required a new point of view. He needed to see God's majestic creation in full daylight. When Elijah left the cave, he could suddenly see mountaintops and vast expanses. He spied the sun and the sky. Elijah discovered that he was only a few divinely orchestrated steps away from an entirely different perspective.

Why did God speak in a whisper? Perhaps Elijah was weary of fire and shouting. Maybe he needed to hear God's gentle voice speaking into his soul. Though we often look for God in the spectacular, our most profound divine encounters often occur during mundane moments. On Mount Carmel, Elijah experienced something remarkable, but he was ready to resign by the next day. After Elijah heard God's still small voice speak to the depths of his soul, Scripture never indicates that Elijah desired to quit again.

CONNECT

God didn't want Elijah to remain in a cave, and He doesn't want you to remain in a wilderness or dark place either. Take your focus off your surroundings and refocus on God. "We become wise when we take our questions to God and receive His answers" (*Overflow*, 116).

➤   What perspectives do you need to change so you are ready to hear from God?

➤ What instructions has God given you that you have not followed?

RE-COMMISSIONED

Then the Lord said to him, "Go and return by the way you came to the Wilderness of Damascus. When you arrive, you are to anoint Hazael as king over Aram. You are to anoint Jehu son of Nimshi as king over Israel and Elisha son of Shaphat from Abel-meholah as prophet in your place. Then Jehu will put to death whoever escapes the sword of Hazael, and Elisha will put to death whoever escapes the sword of Jehu. But I will leave 7,000 in Israel—every knee that has not bowed to Baal and every mouth that has not kissed him."

Elijah left there and found Elisha son of Shaphat as he was plowing. Twelve teams of oxen were in front of him, and he was with the twelfth team. Elijah walked by him and threw his mantle over him. Elisha left the oxen, ran to follow Elijah, and said, "Please let me kiss my father and mother, and then I will follow you."

"Go on back," he replied, "for what have I done to you?"

So he turned back from following him, took the team of oxen, and slaughtered them. With the oxen's wooden yoke and plow, he cooked the meat and gave it to the people, and they ate. Then he left, followed Elijah, and served him. (1 Kings 19:15-21)

Elijah shared plenty of complaints with his Lord. God listened, but He never responded. Instead, He set the agenda for their conversation. He said Elijah would appoint two kings and his successor, Elisha. Elijah thought his ministry was finished, but he discovered he had yet to make his most lasting contributions. God also told Elijah to go. God has no patience for pity parties!

He knows sometimes the best remedy for our problems is for us to move forward once again.

Elijah was ready to quit despite having more to offer others than ever before. Instead, God connected him with an enthusiastic, passionate protégé. Perhaps that partnership was as much for Elijah's benefit as for Elisha's! Elisha's enthusiasm may have reminded Elijah of the zeal he himself had possessed before he grew weary in God's service.

OVERFLOW

➤   Return to God's presence and listen for His voice. Does He have a fresh assignment for you?

➤   How are you pushing your agenda on God? How are you seeking His agenda for you?

➤   How are you investing in the next generation? How is that investment affecting you?

"Whether God was preparing Elijah to perform miracles, or teaching Elijah to trust Him for the impossible, or restoring his faith in times of trials and opposition, the key to Elijah's ministry was God. . . God is seeking people today who will allow Him to work in their lives just as he did with Elijah. Many people long for the power of Elijah, but far fewer are prepared to pay the price of Elijah." (*Overflow*, 134-135).

ACCOUNTABILITY

Complete before your next small group session:

➤ What is preventing you from experiencing spiritual overflow in your life? Spend time prayerfully considering the influences you are allowing into your thoughts, decision making, and relationships that are clouding your walk with God.

➤ What price are you willing to pay to hear from God?

➤ Spend time prayerfully reviewing and answering the questions from this session.

➤ Read Section 3, Chapters 10 – 12 in *Living Out of The Overflow: Serving Out of Your Intimacy with God.*

LIVING OUT OF THE OVERFLOW

SERVING OUT OF YOUR INTIMACY WITH GOD

GROUP SESSION 5: FEELING STUCK

GROUP SESSION 5: FEELING STUCK

ACCOUNTABILITY

Discuss your answers from the *OVERFLOW* section in **Group Session 4**:

➤ What is preventing you from experiencing spiritual overflow in your life?

➤ What price are you willing to pay to hear from God?

The thought of missing out on something great can cause discouragement, regret, and fear. We can easily become trapped into thinking past decisions, missed opportunities, or present consequences disqualify us from serving God. But God still has a plan and calling for our life. We are never too old or too deep into the wilderness for God to use us. Moses spent forty years in the wilderness with a disobedient people and wondered if the initial vision God gave him would ever come to fruition. "Then to Moses' surprise, God found him in the wilderness and announced that his life's calling had never been revoked" (*Overflow*, 139).

The entire Israelite community entered the Wilderness of Zin in the first month, and they settled in Kadesh. Miriam died and was buried there. (Numbers 20:1)

GOD'S WILL AND DIFFICULT PLACES

Moses dreamed of leading the Israelites into the Promised Land. God used Moses to deliver them from slavery in Egypt, but he was forced to wait for forty years in the wilderness before resuming his goal. "Before God led His people onward to fresh victories, He made them address their previous failures" (*Overflow*, 147). Would the next generation of Israelites demonstrate the same faithlessness their parents had? Would they trust God and move forward?

CONNECT

> ➤ Describe a dream or calling God has planted in your heart.

> ➤ Have you avoided or given up on a dream or calling because of your difficult circumstances?

➤ Describe some challenging places you have gone while following God's call. How did God provide for you in those difficult situations?

There was no water for the community, so they assembled against Moses and Aaron. The people quarreled with Moses and said, "If only we had perished when our brothers perished before the Lord. Why have you brought the Lord's assembly into this wilderness for us and our livestock to die here? Why have you led us up from Egypt to bring us to this evil place? It's not a place of grain, figs, vines, and pomegranates, and there is no water to drink!" (Numbers 20:2-5)

COMPLAINERS

To Moses' disappointment, the people complained. Moses had waited 40 years to lead a new generation of Israelites into the Promised Land, but they grumbled as much as their parents had. Why did God continue to allow Moses to face criticism and opposition after so many years of faithful service?

Ironically, the Israelites complained that there were no figs, grain, or pomegranates at Kadesh. But if their parents had trusted God forty years earlier, they would have enjoyed those provisions in abundance (Numbers 13:23). The Israelites wanted to reap the rewards of obedience before they obeyed. They wanted to dwell in the wilderness but enjoy the fruits of the Promised Land!

A close, faithful relationship with God is a precursor to obedience. "Whenever God launches a new advance, some people are so disoriented to Him that they criticize and complain rather than worship and advance" (*Overflow*, 161). Many people are not in tune with God and do not have a heart of obedience. They are chasing their own dreams and do not trust God to fulfill His promises.

CONNECT

➤ Why do people complain? Are you a complainer?

➤ In your group, discuss ways you can guard your heart against discontentment.

➤ How do complainers harm their leader? How can leaders guard themselves from complainers?

Then Moses and Aaron went from the presence of the assembly to the doorway of the tent of meeting. They fell down with their faces to the ground, and the glory of the Lord appeared to them. (Numbers 20:6)

SEEKING THE GLORY OF THE LORD

Attempting to defend ourselves from critics comes naturally, and we are often quick to point out the error in other people's hearts. "Although we cannot always determine our circumstances, we have absolute control over our response. Though others may act in an ungodly manner toward us, we are entirely free to respond in the spirit of Christ" (*Overflow*, 166).

Moses could have descended into a protracted, profitless argument with his detractors. Instead, he broke away from the grumblers and hurriedly made his way into God's presence. In that sacred place, he fell on his face and waited for a word from the Lord. Scripture doesn't reveal how long Moses waited, but he clearly didn't intend to leave until he heard from God.

"God granted Moses something far greater than a solution to his problems. God gave Moses Himself. In that sacred tent, God's glory fell" (*Overflow*, 171). In difficult times, we tend to want an answer to our problem rather than an experience with the One who has the answers. When God's glory fell on Moses, He told Moses exactly what to do next. God always has the solution to our problems.

OVERFLOW

➤ How much time do you spend listening to, arguing with, or focusing on your critics? Do you spend the same amount of time or more on your face before God?

➤ What issues do you currently need to take to God?

A complaining heart is a dissatisfied heart. People often act in the way they see their leader behaving. If leaders complain and grumble, their followers will likely complain and grumble too. We cannot control other people's actions, but we are responsible for making sure our heart is clean before the Lord. Paul had many reasons to complain, but he learned to be content in all circumstances (Philippians 4:11). Understanding how God has and will continue to provide for our needs paves the way for a true heart of gratitude.

ACCOUNTABILITY

Complete before your next small group session:

➤ Spend time in prayer asking God to show you areas of discontentment in your heart. Write down what He reveals.

➤ Have you been more interested in getting answers or spending time in the presence of the One who has the answers? Spend an open-ended amount of time in God's presence this week.

➤ Prayerfully review and answer the questions from this session.

➤ Read Section 3, Chapters 13 – 15 in *Living Out of The Overflow: Serving Out of Your Intimacy with God.*

LIVING OUT OF THE OVERFLOW

SERVING OUT OF YOUR INTIMACY WITH GOD

GROUP SESSION 6: HONOR THROUGH OBEDIENCE

GROUP SESSION 6: HONOR THROUGH OBEDIENCE

ACCOUNTABILITY

Discuss your answers from the *OVERFLOW* section in **Group Session 5**:

➤ How much time do you spend listening to, arguing with, or focusing on your critics? Do you spend the same amount of time or more on your face before God?

➤ What issues do you currently need to take to God?

Faulty expectations lead to disappointment. If we assume God will shield us from every difficulty, critic, or opponent, we are bound to experience dissatisfaction. But if we trust that He will guide us through challenges, we will not be caught off guard when difficulties arise. Problems provide an opportunity for God to demonstrate His power in our lives. God's primary purpose for our life is not our comfort but His glory!

The Lord spoke to Moses, "Take the staff and assemble the community. You and your brother Aaron are to speak to the rock while they watch, and it will yield its water. You will bring out water for them from the rock and provide drink for the community and their livestock."

So Moses took the staff from the Lord's presence just as He had commanded him. (Numbers 20:7-9)

SPEAK TO THE ROCK

God did not merely give Moses principles to follow; He provided specific instructions. Moses was to take his rod, gather the leaders, and speak to the rock. Years earlier, Moses had dealt with a similar issue at Rephidim (Exodus 17:1-7). On that occasion, God told Moses to strike the rock. This story raises an important question: why didn't God tell Moses to use the same method he had employed successfully last time?

God desires for His people to glorify Him. "He was giving Moses a choice. Moses could trust God to do a greater work through his life than He had done before, or he could resort to methods that had been successful in the past" (*Overflow,* 180). Few things are as seductive to the Church as previous success! God does not want us to trust a method. He wants us to trust Him. He changed the instructions so Moses would not rely on a formula but on the God who granted him his previous victory. Likewise, God wants to take our leadership to higher levels each year so we bring Him greater glory and produce more fruit in our life and ministry.

CONNECT

➤ List and discuss some occasions when you were tempted to trust more in a method than in God. Why are methods and previous successes so seductive?

➤   How is God doing a greater work through you today than He was five or ten years ago?

➤   If your ministry remains the same year after year, why might that be?

➤   Why does God prefer that you trust Him rather than a method or program?

Moses and Aaron summoned the assembly in front of the rock, and Moses said to them, "Listen, you rebels! Must we bring water out of this rock for you?" Then Moses raised his hand and struck the rock twice with his staff. (Numbers 20:10-11a)

LISTEN, YOU REBELS!

Until this point, Moses handled the crisis extremely well. But then he came unglued. Though he accused his followers of being rebellious, he was the biggest rebel of them all. None of the people Moses condemned were excluded from Canaan because of their behavior that day, but he was. Paradoxically, the sins that most anger us in others are often the ones we battle ourselves.

Exasperated, Moses uttered the fateful words, *"Must we bring water out of this rock for you?"* "Moses served God for so long that he began to identify his efforts with God's work. He dared to touch God's glory" (*Overflow*, 193). He failed to hallow God before his people and then he struck the rock twice. Why twice? Because he was acting in his own strength, not God's. Many prideful ministers have worn themselves out feverishly striking the rock when God told them to speak to it. People never burn out when serving in God's power, but they regularly grow weary when ministering in their own strength.

CONNECT

➤ Why do we often become angry at people who struggle with the same sins we do?

➤ Describe a time when you gave your followers a piece of your mind instead of delivering a message from God. What was the result of that message? Whom did your words glorify? Whom did they dishonor?

➤ Why do so many ministers burn out and quit?

➤ In what ways might you be in danger of touching God's glory?

. . . so that a great amount of water gushed out, and the community and their livestock drank.

But the Lord said to Moses and Aaron, "Because you did not trust Me to show My holiness in the sight of the Israelites, you will not bring this assembly into the land I have given them." These are the waters of Meribah, where the Israelites quarreled with the Lord, and He showed His holiness to them." (Numbers 20:11b-13)

HALLOWED

Moses failed to obey God's instructions. Nevertheless, God sent water out of the rock anyway. Why? Perhaps because God's people would be in a sorry state if He withheld His provision every time a leader acted foolishly! God blesses His people primarily in two ways: *through* a leader or *despite* the leader.

Moses failed to hallow God. But the concluding verse indicates that God hallowed Himself. Leaders can glorify God by their obedience, or God can glorify Himself as He disciplines leaders for their disobedience.

➤ In what ways might you not be hallowing God before your followers?

➤   How has God disciplined you publicly?

➤   How is God presently blessing your people? Is He bestowing these blessings because of you or in spite of you?

CONTINUED ACCOUNTABILITY

Leading God's people is a precarious, confusing, exhausting, rewarding undertaking! Effective leadership flows from the overflow of our walk with God. Apart from Christ, we can do nothing (John 15:5). "Elijah and Moses are classic examples, not of what talented people can do for God, but of what almighty God can accomplish through any person wholly surrendered to Him" (*Overflow*, 207).

➤   What lessons have you learned from Elijah that apply to your life and ministry?

➤ What lessons have you learned from Moses that you can apply to your life and ministry?

➤ What is God waiting for you to surrender in your life so you are prepared to accomplish something great for His glory?

➤ What adjustments does God want you to make in your leadership?

➤ Do you need God's glory to fall fresh on you and your ministry? If so, what plans do you have to fall on your face before Him?

Remember this: You are only one fresh encounter with God away from the greatest ministry you have ever had!

ABOUT THE AUTHOR

 **Dr. Richard Blackaby** is the president of Blackaby Ministries International (www.blackaby.org). He has authored or co-authored thirty-five books and speaks internationally on leadership in the church, business, and home. He regularly works with Christian CEOs of major companies in the USA and around the world, helping them align their life and business with God's agenda. Richard has also served as a pastor and a seminary president. He lives with his wife, Lisa, in Atlanta. They have three children and four grandsons.

Twitter: @richardblackaby
Facebook: Dr. Richard Blackaby
Blog: www.RichardBlackaby.com

Blackaby Ministries International (www.blackaby.org) is dedicated to helping people experience God. It has books and resources to assist Christians in the areas of experiencing God, spiritual leadership, revival, the marketplace, and the family. There are also resources for young adults and children. Please contact them at:

Facebook: Blackaby Ministries International
Twitter: @ExperiencingGod
Mobile App: Blackaby ministries int
Website: www.blackaby.org

Blackaby Ministries International (www.blackaby.org) is dedicated to helping people experience God. It has books and resources to assist Christians in the areas of experiencing God, spiritual leadership, revival, the marketplace, and the family. There are also resources for young adults and children. Please contact them at:

Facebook: Blackaby Ministries International
Twitter: @ExperiencingGod
Mobile App: Blackaby ministries int
Website: www.blackaby.org

WWW.BLACKABY.ORG

BLACKABY RESOURCES

To discover all the resources BMI offers please see
www.blackabystore.org

BLACKABY LEADERSHIP COACHING

Blackaby Ministries provides coaching-based solutions to challenges
faced by ministry and marketplace leaders. To learn more, go to
www.blackabycoaching.org

BLACKABY REVITALIZATION MINISTRY

If you sense God wants more for your church than what
you are currently experiencing, we want to help.
www.blackaby.org/revitalization

THE COLLISION

God is actively at work in the lives of the younger generation and
Blackaby Ministries is stepping out to join in this exciting activity.
www.thecollision.org

CPSIA information can be obtained
at www.ICGtesting.com
Printed in the USA
BVHW062304300121
599034BV00002B/12

9 781732 093928